COLDPL

COLDPLAY

CHORD SONGBOOK

Wise Publications
London/New York/Paris/Sydney/Copenhagen/Madrid/Tokyo

Exclusive Distributors:

Music Sales Limited
8/9 Frith Street,
London W1D 3JB, England.
Music Sales Pty Limited
120 Rothschild Avenue,
Rosebery, NSW 2018, Australia.

Order No. AM970904
ISBN 0-7119-8915-X
This book © Copyright 2001 by Wise Publications

Compiled by Nick Crispin
Music arranged by Matt Cowe
Music engraved by The Pitts

Printed in the United Kingdom by
Caligraving Limited, Thetford, Nolfolk.

Your Guarantee of Quality
As publishers, we strive to produce every book
to the highest commercial standards.
This book has been carefully designed to minimise awkward
page turns and to make playing from it a real pleasure.
Particular care has been given to specifying acid-free,
neutral-sized paper made from pulps which have not been
elemental chlorine bleached. This pulp is from farmed sustainable
forests and was produced with special regard for the environment.
Throughout, the printing and binding have been planned to
ensure a sturdy, attractive publication which should give years
of enjoyment. If your copy fails to meet our high standards,
please inform us and we will gladly replace it.

Music Sales' complete catalogue describes thousands
of titles and is available in full colour sections by subject,
direct from Music Sales Limited. Please state your areas of interest
and send a cheque/postal order for £1.50 for postage to:
Music Sales Limited, Newmarket Road,
Bury St. Edmunds, Suffolk IP33 3YB.

www.musicsales.com

Relative Tuning

The guitar can be tuned with the aid of pitch pipes or dedicated electronic guitar tuners which are available through your local music dealer. If you do not have a tuning device, you can use relative tuning. Estimate the pitch of the 6th string as near as possible to E or at least a comfortable pitch (not too high, as you might break other strings in tuning up). Then, while checking the various positions on the diagram, place a finger from your left hand on the:

5th fret of the E or 6th string and **tune the open A** (or 5th string) to the note (A)

5th fret of the A or 5th string and **tune the open D** (or 4th string) to the note (D)

5th fret of the D or 4th string and **tune the open G** (or 3rd string) to the note (G)

4th fret of the G or 3rd string and **tune the open B** (or 2nd string) to the note (B)

5th fret of the B or 2nd string and **tune the open E** (or 1st string) to the note (E)

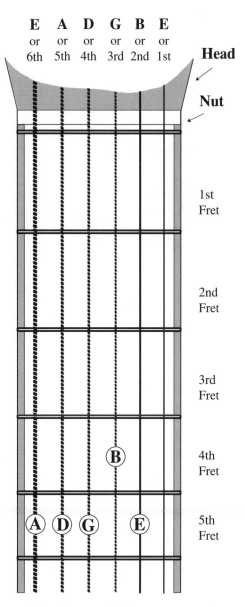

Reading Chord Boxes

Chord boxes are diagrams of the guitar neck viewed head upwards, face on as illustrated. The top horizontal line is the nut, unless a higher fret number is indicated, the others are the frets.

The vertical lines are the strings, starting from E (or 6th) on the left to E (or 1st) on the right.

The black dots indicate where to place your fingers.

Strings marked with an O are played open, not fretted. Strings marked with an X should not be played.

The curved bracket indicates a 'barre' – hold down the strings under the bracket with your first finger, using your other fingers to fret the remaining notes.

7

Don't Panic

Words & Music by
Words & Music by Guy Berryman, Jon Buckland, Will Champion & Chris Martin

Intro ∥ Fmaj7 | Fmaj7 | Fmaj7 | Fmaj7 ∥

Verse 1
Am   C   Fmaj7 Fmaj9
Bones sinking like stones, all that we've fought for.
Am   C   Fmaj7 Fmaj9#11
Homes, places we've grown, all of us are done for.

Chorus 1
Dmadd9   Am*
But we live in a beautiful world,
G6
Yeah we do, yeah we do,
Dmadd9 | Fmaj7 Fmaj9 | Fmaj7 Fmaj9 ∥
We live in a beautiful world

Verse 2 As Verse 1

Chorus 2 As Chorus 1

Solo 1 | Am | C | Fmaj7 | Fmaj9 |

| Am | C | Fmaj7 | Fmaj9#11 ∥

Chorus 3 As Chorus 1

Solo 2 As Solo 1

Verse 3
Am   C   Fmaj7 Fmaj9
Oh, all that I know, there's nothing here to run from,
     Am   C   Fmaj7
'Cause yeah, everybody here's got somebody to lean on.

Bigger Stronger

Words & Music by
Words & Music by Guy Berryman, Jon Buckland, Will Champion & Chris Martin

Intro | Am | Am   ‖

Verse 1
                  Am   **F#m7♭5**   **C**
I wanna be bigger, stronger, drive a faster car

To take me anywhere in seconds,
           Dsus2   **Am**
To take me anywhere I wanna go
                           F#m7♭5   **C**
And drive around a faster car.

I will settle for nothing less,
        Dsus2   **Am** | **Am**   ‖
I will settle for nothing less.

Verse 2
                  Am   **F#m7♭5**   **C**
I wanna be bigger, stronger, drive a faster car.

At the touch of a button
           Dsus2   **Am**
I can go anywhere I wanna go
                           F#m7♭5   **C**
And drive around my faster   car.

I will settle for nothing less,
        Dsus2   **Am** | **Am**   ‖
I will settle for nothing less.

Chorus 1

                  Dm   **Dm/C#**   **Gm**
I think I want to change my   altitude,

      C   **Gm**   **Em**   **A**
I think I want to change my oxygen,

                  Dm   **Dm/C#** **Gm** **C**   **Gm**
I think I want to change my air, my   atmosphere,

   Em   **A** | **A** ||
I want to reach out.

Solo 1   ‖: **Am** | **D** | **Am** | **D**   :‖

Verse 3

                 Am   **F#m7b5**   **C**
I wanna be bigger, stronger, drive a faster car

To take me anywhere in seconds,

            Dsus2   **Am**
To take me anywhere I wanna go

                     F#m7b5 **C**
And drive around my faster car.

I will settle for nothing less,

      Dsus2   **Am** | **Am** ||
I will settle for nothing less.

Chorus 2

                  Dm   **Dm/C#**   **Gm**
I think I need to change my   altitude,

      C   **Gm**   **Em**   **A**
I think I want to change my oxygen,

                  Dm   **Dm/C#** **Gm** **C**   **Gm**
I think I want to change my air, my   atmosphere,

   Em   **A** | **A** ||
I want to reach out.

Solo 2   ‖: **Fmaj7** | **G**   **C** | **D** | **D**   :‖ *Play 4 times*

       ‖: **Am** | **D** | **Am** | **D**   :‖

Verse 4

Am   **D**   **Am**   **D**
Bigger and better, bigger and better,

Am   **D**   **Am**   **D**
Bigger and better, bigger and better,

Am   **F#m7b5**   **C**
Bigger, stronger drive a faster car,

                             Dsus2   **Am**
At the touch of a button I can go anywhere I wanna go.

Brothers And Sisters

Words & Music by
Guy Berryman, Jon Buckland, Will Champion & Chris Martin

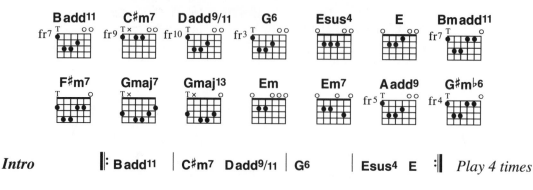

Intro   ‖: Badd¹¹ | C♯m⁷ Dadd⁹/¹¹ | G⁶ | Esus⁴ E :‖ *Play 4 times*

Verse 1
Bmadd¹¹   F♯m⁷   Gmaj⁷
Brothers and sisters unite,
       Gmaj¹³ Bmadd¹¹ F♯m⁷   Gmaj⁷
It's the time of your   lives, it's the time of your lives,
     Gmaj¹³ Bmadd¹¹
Breakdown, break - down,
   F♯m⁷   Gmaj⁷   Em
Got to spread love around, got to spread it around.

Verse 2
Bmadd¹¹   F♯m⁷   Gmaj⁷
Brothers and sisters feel fine,
       Gmaj¹³ Bmadd¹¹ F♯m⁷   Gmaj⁷
It's the time of your   lives, it's the time of your lives,
     Gmaj¹³ Bmadd¹¹
There's no sound, no sound,
   F♯m⁷   Gmaj⁷   Em
Like this feeling you found, like this feeling you found.

Chorus 1
      Badd¹¹ C♯m⁷
But just stay down,
       Dadd⁹/¹¹ C♯m⁷
'Cause sometimes you feel,
   Badd¹¹ C♯m⁷
So stay down.

Dadd9/11   C#m7 Gmaj7

cont.   And sometimes you feel,

                Em7   Aadd9   Gmaj7
And it's me they're looking for,

                Em7   Aadd9   Gmaj7
And it's me, I will never survive,

                  Em7   Aadd9
But we'll be around some more.

| Gmaj7 | Gmaj13 | Gmaj7 | Gmaj13 ||

        Bmadd11   F#m7   Gmaj7
Verse 3   Brothers and sisters unite,

                Gmaj13 Bmadd11   F#m7   Gmaj7
It's the time of your   lives, it's the time of your lives,

                Gmaj13 Bmadd11
Breakdown, break - down,

          F#m7   Gmaj7   Em
Got to spread love around, got to spread it all round.

                Badd11 C#m7
Chorus 2 But just stay down,

                        Dadd9/11   C#m7
And sometimes you'll feel,

                Badd11 C#m7
So stay around.

                        Dadd9/11   C#m7 Gmaj7
And sometimes you'll feel,

                Em7   Aadd9   Gmaj7
And it's me they're looking for,

                Em7   Aadd9   Gmaj7
And it's me, I will never survive,

                Em7   Aadd9
But we'll be around some more.

| Gmaj7 | Gmaj13 | Gmaj7 | Gmaj13 ||

Outro | Badd11 | C#m7 Dadd9/11 | G6 | | Esus4 E |
                                            It's gonna be al -

          | Badd11 | Badd11 G#m♭6 | F#m7 | E |
        - right.   It's gonna be al -

          | Badd11 | C#m7 Dadd9/11 | G6 | | F#m7 |
        - right.   It's gonna be al -

          | Badd11 | C#m7 Dadd9/11 | G6 | | F#m7 ||
        - right.

Careful Where You Stand

Words & Music by
Guy Berryman, Jon Buckland, Will Champion & Chris Martin

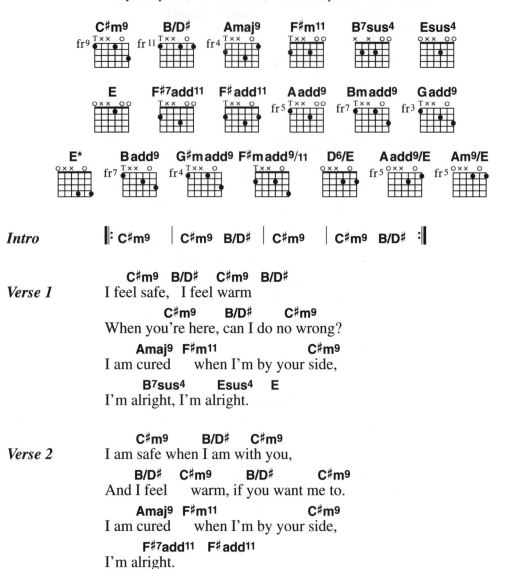

Intro   ‖: C#m9 | C#m9 B/D# | C#m9 | C#m9 B/D# :‖

Verse 1

      C#m9 B/D#   C#m9 B/D#
I feel safe, I feel warm

         C#m9   B/D#   C#m9
When you're here, can I do no wrong?

     Amaj9 F#m11   C#m9
I am cured   when I'm by your side,

       B7sus4   Esus4   E
I'm alright, I'm alright.

Verse 2

      C#m9   B/D#   C#m9
I am safe when I am with you,

       B/D# C#m9   B/D#   C#m9
And I feel   warm, if you want me to.

     Amaj9 F#m11   C#m9
I am cured   when I'm by your side,

      F#7add11 F#add11
I'm alright.

‖ F#7add11 F#add11 | Aadd9 Amaj9 | Aadd9 ‖

Chorus 1

Bmadd9   Gadd9   E*   Gadd9
Careful where you stand, my love,

Bmadd9   Gadd9   E*   Gadd9
Careful where you lay your head.

cont.

Badd9 G♯madd9 Gadd9
It's true, _____ we're always there

   F♯madd 9/11 D6/E | E* | D6/E | E* ||
Looking out for one another.

Verse 3

  C♯m9   B/D♯ C♯m9
I feel safe when I am with you,

  B/D♯ C♯m9   B/D♯ C♯m9
And I feel warm, when you want me to.

  Amaj9 F♯m11   C♯m9
I am cured when you're all alone,

  F♯7add11 F♯add11
I'm alright.

| Aadd9 Amaj9 | Aadd9 ||

Chorus 2

Bmadd9   Gadd9 E* Gadd9
Careful where you stand, my love,

Bmadd9   Gadd9 E* Gadd9
Careful where you lay your head.

 Badd9 G♯madd9 Gadd9
It's true, _____ we're always

   F♯madd 9/11 E*
Looking out for one another.

Link 1 | Aadd9/E | Am9/E | E* | Aadd9/E | Am9/E | E* ||

Bridge 1

Aadd9/E Am9/E E*
So I'd like a quiet town, please,

  Aadd9/E Am9/E Bmadd9 | Gadd9 | E* | Gadd9 ||
Yeah, I'd like a quiet town. _____

Link 2 | Bmadd9 | Gadd9 | E* | Gadd9 ||

Bridge 2

Bmadd9 Gadd9 E*   Gadd9
Ooh now, _____ now, _____ ooh. _____

Bmadd9 Gadd9 E*   Gadd9
Ooh now, _____ now, _____ ooh. _____

  Badd9 G♯madd9 Gadd9 F♯madd9/11
And care - ful where you stand,

  Badd9 G♯madd9 Gadd9 F♯madd9/11
And care - ful where you stand. ____

| Badd9 | G♯madd9 | Gadd9 | Gadd9 ‖

Easy To Please

Words & Music by
Guy Berryman, Jon Buckland, Will Champion & Chris Martin

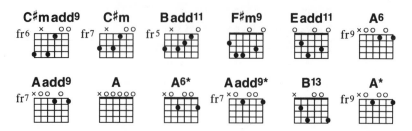

Tune guitar (from bottom string): D, G, D, G, B, D, then Capo second fret

Intro | C#madd9 | C#madd9 ‖

Verse 1

  C#m   Badd11
Love, I hope we get old,

     F#m9   Eadd11
I hope we can find a way of seeing it all.

   C#m   Badd11
Love, I hope we can be,

      F#m9
I hope I can find a way

        A6 Aadd9 A6 Aadd9
Of letting you see

    A A6* Aadd9* A6* A
That I'm so ea - - sy to please,

A6* Aadd9* A6*
So ea - - - (sy.)

| B13 Aadd9* A* | B13 Aadd9* A* |
- - sy.

| B13 Aadd9* A* | B13 Aadd9* A* ‖

Verse 2

       C#m   Badd11
Love, I hope we grow old,

             F#m9   Eadd11
I hope we can find a way of seeing it all.

       C#m   Badd11
Love, I hope we can be,

           F#m9
I hope I can find a way

               A6 Aadd9 A6 Aadd9
Of letting you see

        A A6* Aadd9* A6*   A
That I'm so   ea - - sy to please,

A6* Aadd9* A6*
So   ea - - - (sy.)

| B13 | Aadd9* | A* | B13 | Aadd9* | A* |
- - sy.

| B13 | Aadd9* | A* | B13 | Aadd9* | A* ‖

Everything's Not Lost

Words & Music by
Guy Berryman, Jon Buckland, Will Champion & Chris Martin

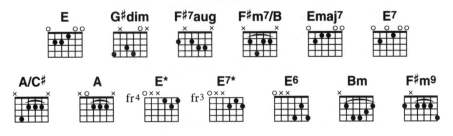

Verse 1

      E   G♯dim   F♯7aug   E
And when I counted up my demons,

            G♯dim   F♯7aug E
Saw there was one for every day,

            G♯dim   F♯7aug   F♯m7/B
But with the good ones on my shoulders

                    E
I drove the other ones away.

Chorus 1

           Emaj7   E7   F♯7aug E
So if you ever feel neglected,

          Emaj7   E7   A/C♯ E
And if you think all is lost,

          Emaj7   E7   A/C♯ A
Well, I'll be counting up my demons, yeah,

          F♯m7/B   E
Hoping everything's not lost.

Link 1   ‖: E* | E7* E6 | E* | E7* E6 :‖

Verse 2

      E   G♯dim   F♯7aug   E
When you thought that it was over,

         G♯dim   F♯7aug E
You could feel it all around.

            G♯dim   F♯7aug   F♯m7/B
When everybody's out to get you,

                 E
Don't you let it drag you down.

Chorus 2   As Chorus 1

Link 2   ‖: E* | E7* E6 | E* | E7* E6 :‖

Chorus 3   As Chorus 1

Outro

                  E*   E7* E6
Singing out ah, ah ah yeah, ah ah yeah,
E*   E7* E6   E*
Ah ah yeah, and everything's not lost,
                E7* E6   E*
So come on, yeah, ah ah yeah,
              E7*   E6   E*
Come on, yeah, and everything's not lost.

              E7* E6   E*
Ah ah yeah, ah ah yeah,
              E7* E6   E*
Ah ah yeah, and everything's not lost,
             E7* E6   E*
Come on yeah, ah ah yeah,
              E7* E6
A-come on yeah.

E   Bm   F♯m9
  A-come on yeah, ah ah yeah,
                      E
Come on yeah, and everything's not lost.
       Bm   F♯m9
Sing out yeah, ah ah yeah,
                      E
Come on yeah, and everything's not lost.
       Bm   F♯m9
Come on yeah, ah ah yeah,
                  E   Bm F♯m
Sing out yeah, and everything's not lost.

For You

Words & Music by
Guy Berryman, Jon Buckland, Will Champion & Chris Martin

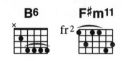

B6   **F#m11**

Intro | B6 | B6 |

‖: B6 | F#m11 | B6 | F#m11 :‖

Verse 1

B6   F#m11
    If you're lost and feel alone,
B6   F#m11
    Circumnavigate the globe,
B6   F#m11
    All you ever have to hope for too.
B6   F#m11
    And the way you seem to flow,
B6   F#m11
    Circumnavigate and hope,
B6   F#m11   B6   F#m11
    And I seem to lose control, with you.

Chorus 1

B6   F#m11
Ah, _____
B6   F#m11
Ah, _____
B6   F#m11
Ah, _____
B6   F#m11
Ah. _____

Link 1   ‖: B6 | F#m11 | B6 | F#m11 :‖

Verse 2

B6   F#m11
  Every one of us is hurt,

B6   F#m11
  And every one of us is scarred,

B6   F#m11   B6   F#m11
  Every one of us is scared but not you.

     B6   F#m11
And when your eyes close,

B6   F#m11
  Your head hurts,

B6   F#m11   B6   F#m11
  Your eyes like stone.

Chorus 2

B6   F#m11
Ah, _____

B6   F#m11
Ah, _____

B6   F#m11
Ah, _____

B6   F#m11
Ah. _____

Link 2

| B6 | F#m11 | B6 | F#m11 ‖

Verse 3

B6   F#m11
  Every one of us is scared,

B6   F#m11
  Every one of us is hurt,

B6   F#m11   B6   F#m11
  Every one has hope for you.

Outro

       B6   F#m11
‖: For you,   :‖   *Play 6 times*

       B6   F#m11
For you.

| B6 | F#m11 |

       B6   F#m11
For you.

       B6   F#m11
For you.

| B6 | F#m11 | B6   ‖

Help Is Round The Corner

Words & Music by
Guy Berryman, Jon Buckland, Will Champion & Chris Martin

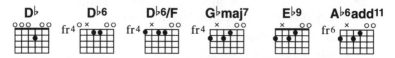

D♭   D♭6   D♭6/F   G♭maj7   E♭9   A♭6add11

Tune guitar (from bottom string): D♭, A♭, D♭, G♭, D♭, F

Intro | D♭ | D♭6 | D♭ | D♭6 ||

Verse 1

D♭   D♭6
Stuck here in the middle of nowhere

D♭   D♭6
With a headache, and a heavy heart.

D♭   D♭6
Well, nothing was going quite right here,

D♭   D♭6   D♭6/F
And I'm tired, I can't play my part.

Chorus 1

G♭maj7
Oh, come on, come on,

           E♭9
Oh what a state I'm in,

G♭maj7
Oh, come on, come on,

              E♭9
Why won't it just sink in

D♭   A♭6add11   D♭ A♭6add11
That help is just around the corner for us?

Verse 2

D♭   D♭6
Oh, my head just won't stop aching,

D♭   D♭6
And I'm sat here licking my wounds

D♭   D♭6
And I'm shattered, but it really doesn't matter

D♭   D♭6   D♭6/F
'Cause my rescue is gonna be here soon.

Chorus 2

G♭maj7
    Oh, come on, come on,

        E♭9
Oh what a state I'm in,

G♭maj7
    Oh, come on, come on,

        E♭9
Why won't it just sink in

  D♭   **A♭6add11**   **D♭**   **A♭6add11**
That help is just around the corner for us? _____

  D♭   **A♭6add11**   **D♭**   **E♭9**
That help is just around the corner for us. _____

      G♭maj7   **A♭6add11**   **D♭**
Oh, that help is just around the corner for us. _____

High Speed

Words & Music by
Guy Berryman, Jon Buckland, Will Champion & Chris Martin

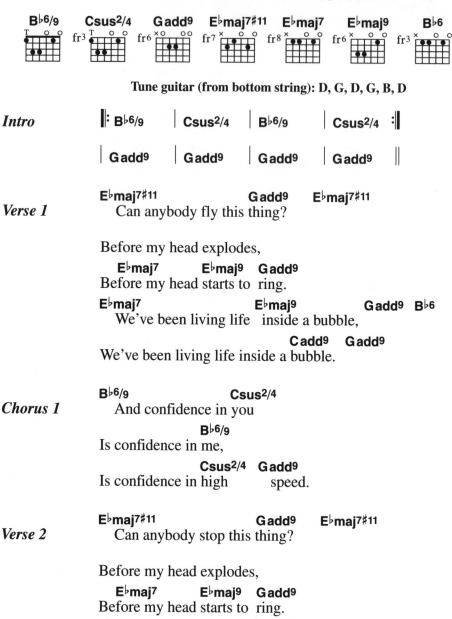

Tune guitar (from bottom string): D, G, D, G, B, D

Intro   ‖: B♭6/9 | Csus2/4 | B♭6/9 | Csus2/4 :‖

| G add9 | G add9 | G add9 | G add9 ‖

Verse 1
E♭maj7#11   G add9   E♭maj7#11
    Can anybody fly this thing?

Before my head explodes,
  E♭maj7   E♭maj9   G add9
Before my head starts to ring.
E♭maj7   E♭maj9   G add9   B♭6
  We've been living life   inside a bubble,
                                          C add9   G add9
We've been living life inside a bubble.

Chorus 1
B♭6/9   Csus2/4
  And confidence in you
                           B♭6/9
Is confidence in me,
                          Csus2/4   G add9
Is confidence in high   speed.

Verse 2
E♭maj7#11   G add9   E♭maj7#11
  Can anybody stop this thing?

Before my head explodes,
  E♭maj7   E♭maj9   G add9
Before my head starts to ring.
E♭maj7   E♭maj9   G add9   B♭6
  We've been living life   inside a bubble,
                                          C add9   G add9
We've been living life inside a bubble.

Chorus 2

B♭6/9   Csus2/4
And confidence in you

           B♭6/9
Is confidence in me,

              Csus2/4   Gadd9
Is confidence in high   speed,

In high speed, high speed.

Link

| Gadd9 | Gadd9 | Gadd9 | Gadd9 ||

Outro

B♭6/9   Csus2/4   B♭6/9
And high speed you want,

            Csus2/4   B♭6/9
High speed you want,

            Csus2/4   B♭6/9   Csus2/4
High speed you want,

                 Gadd9
High speed you want.

‖: Gadd9 | Gadd9   :‖ *Repeat to fade*

No More Keeping My Feet On The Ground

Words & Music by
Guy Berryman, Jon Buckland, Will Champion & Chris Martin

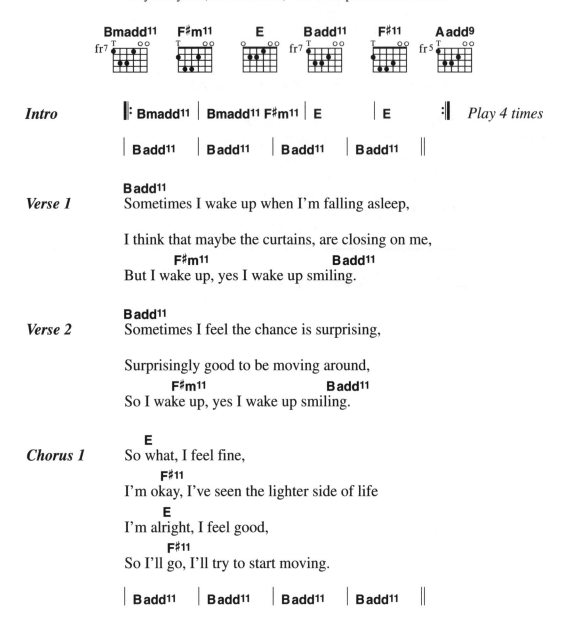

Intro ‖: Bmadd¹¹ | Bmadd¹¹ F♯m¹¹ | E | E :‖ *Play 4 times*

| Badd¹¹ | Badd¹¹ | Badd¹¹ | Badd¹¹ ‖

Verse 1
Badd¹¹
Sometimes I wake up when I'm falling asleep,

I think that maybe the curtains, are closing on me,
F♯m¹¹   **Badd¹¹**
But I wake up, yes I wake up smiling.

Verse 2
Badd¹¹
Sometimes I feel the chance is surprising,

Surprisingly good to be moving around,
F♯m¹¹   **Badd¹¹**
So I wake up, yes I wake up smiling.

Chorus 1
E
So what, I feel fine,

F♯¹¹
I'm okay, I've seen the lighter side of life

E
I'm alright, I feel good,

F♯¹¹
So I'll go, I'll try to start moving.

| Badd¹¹ | Badd¹¹ | Badd¹¹ | Badd¹¹ ‖

Verse 3

Badd11
Sometimes I wake up and I'm falling asleep,

                                                                     F#m11
But I've got to get going, so much that I wanted to do,

                    Badd11   **Aadd9**
But I wake up smiling.

Bridge 1

                                 F#11
And this could be my last chance,

                    Aadd9
Of saving my innocence,

                               F#11
And this could be my last chance,

                               Badd11
No more keeping my feet on the ground.

| **Badd11** | **Badd11** | **Badd11** ‖

Verse 4

Badd11
Sometimes I feel the chance is surprising,

Surprisingly good to be moving around,

        F#m11   **Badd11**
And I move, and I wake up smiling.

Chorus 2

       E
So what, I feel fine,

       F#11
I feel okay, I've seen the lighter side of life

       E
I'm alright, I feel good,

       F#11   **Aadd9**
So I'll go, well it's time to start moving.

Bridge 2   As Bridge 1

Outro

Badd11
And there's nothing to keep them,

There's nothing to keep them down

And there's nothing to keep them,

There's nothing to keep them down.

| **Badd11** | **Badd11** ‖

27

Life Is For Living

Words & Music by
Guy Berryman, Jon Buckland, Will Champion & Chris Martin

Bᵇ   Gm7   Bᵇ/F   F   Eᵇ   fr3 Cm7   Bᵇsus4   F7

Tune guitar (from bottom string): E, A, D, G, B, D

Verse 1
          Bᵇ   Gm7   Bᵇ/F   F
Now I never meant to do you wrong,
  Eᵇ   Cm7   Bᵇ Bᵇsus4 Bᵇ
That's what I came here to say.
          Gm7   Bᵇ/F   F
But if I was wrong then I'm sorry,
      Eᵇ   Cm7   Bᵇ Bᵇsus4 Bᵇ
Then I don't let it stand in our way.

Verse 2
             Gm7   Bᵇ/F   F
'Cause my head just aches when I think of
     Eᵇ   Cm7   Bᵇ Bᵇsus4 Bᵇ
The things that I shouldn't have done,
       Gm7   Bᵇ/F F
But life is for living, we all know,
    Eᵇ   Cm7   Bᵇ Bᵇsus4 Bᵇ
And I don't want to live it alone.

Bridge
     F   F7
Sing ah ah ah,
     Eᵇ
Sing ah ah ah,
          F   F7
And you sing ah ah ah.

Coda
| Bᵇ | Gm7 | Bᵇ/F | F | |

| Eᵇ | Cm7 | Bᵇ Bᵇsus4 | Bᵇ |

| Bᵇ | Gm7 | Bᵇ/F | F |

| Eᵇ | Cm7 | Bᵇ Bᵇsus4 | Bᵇ ‖

Parachutes

Words & Music by
Guy Berryman, Jon Buckland, Will Champion & Chris Martin

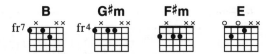

Tune guitar (from bottom string): E, A, B, G, B, D♯

Intro

| B | G♯m | B | G♯m | |
| F♯m | F♯m | E | E | ‖ |

Verse 1

B
In a haze,
G♯m
A stormy haze,
B
I'll be 'round,
    G♯m   **F♯m**
I'll be loving you always,
    E
Always

Verse 2

B
Here I am
    G♯m
And I'll take my time.
B
Here I am
    G♯m   **F♯m**
And I'll wait in line always,
    E
Always.

Only Superstition

Words & Music by
Guy Berryman, Jon Buckland, Will Champion & Chris Martin

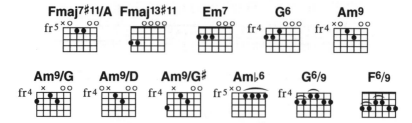

Tune guitar (from bottom string): **D, A, C, G, B, E**

Intro | Fmaj⁷♯¹¹/A | Fmaj⁷♯¹¹/A |

‖: Fmaj¹³♯¹¹ Em⁷ Fmaj¹³♯¹¹ | G⁶   :‖ *Play 4 times*

Verse 1
Am⁹   Am⁹/G   Am⁹/D Am⁹/G
The cardboard head I see

Am⁹   Am⁹/G   Am⁹/D Am⁹/G
Has found its way to me,

Am⁹ Am⁹/G   Am⁹/D   Am⁹/G
It's out and it's out and it's out,

Am⁹   Am⁹/G Am⁹/D Am⁹/G
Making me cry.

Am⁹ Am⁹/G   Am⁹/D Am⁹/G
I   sleep but I will not move,

Am⁹   Am⁹/G   Am⁹/D Am⁹/G
I'm too scared to leave my room,

Am⁹   Am⁹/G   Am⁹/D   Am⁹/G Am⁹ Am⁹/G Am⁹/D Am⁹/G
But I won't be defeated, oh no.

Chorus 1
Fmaj¹³♯¹¹ G⁶   Fmaj¹³♯¹¹
What if cars don't go my way

        G⁶   Fmaj¹³♯¹¹
And it's sure to spoil my day?

        G⁶   Fmaj¹³♯¹¹   G⁶
But in voices loud and clear you say to me;

Fmaj¹³#¹¹   **Em⁷** **G⁶**

"It's only superstition,

Em⁷   **Fmaj¹³#¹¹** **G⁶** **Fmaj¹³#¹¹** **Em⁷** **G⁶**

It's only your   imagination,

Em⁷   **Fmaj¹³#¹¹** **G⁶** **Fmaj¹³#¹¹**   **Em⁷**

It's only all   the things that you fear

Fmaj¹³#¹¹ **G⁶**   **Em⁷**   **Fmaj¹³#¹¹** **G⁶**

And the   things from which you can't escape."

| **Fmaj¹³#¹¹** **Em⁷** **Fmaj¹³#¹¹** | **G⁶** **Em⁷** **Fmaj¹³#¹¹** **G⁶** ‖

Verse 2

Am⁹   **Am⁹/G**   **Am⁹/D**   **Am⁹/G**

Keep clean for the thousandth time,

Am⁹   **Am⁹/G**   **Am⁹/D** **Am⁹/G**

Stand still and wait in line,

Am⁹   **Am⁹/G**   **Am⁹/D** **Am⁹/G**

Some numbers are better than others,

    Am⁹ **Am⁹/G** **Am⁹/D** **Am⁹/G**

Oh no.

Chorus 2

Fmaj¹³#¹¹ **G⁶**   **Fmaj¹³#¹¹**

What if cars don't go my way

        G⁶   **Fmaj¹³#¹¹**

And it's sure to spoil my day?

        G⁶   **Fmaj¹³#¹¹**   **G⁶**

But in voices loud and clear you say to me;

        Fmaj¹³#¹¹   **Em⁷** **G⁶**

"It's only superstition,

Em⁷   **Fmaj¹³#¹¹** **G⁶** **Fmaj¹³#¹¹** **Em⁷** **G⁶**

It's only your   imagination,

Em⁷   **Fmaj¹³#¹¹** **G⁶** **Fmaj¹³#¹¹**   **Em⁷**

It's only all   of the things that you fear

Fmaj¹³#¹¹ **G⁶**   **Em⁷**   **Fmaj¹³#¹¹** **G⁶**

And the   things which you cannot ex - plain."

| **Fmaj¹³#¹¹** **Em⁷** **Fmaj¹³#¹¹** | **G⁶** **Em⁷** **Fmaj¹³#¹¹** **G⁶** ‖

Bridge

Fmaj¹³#¹¹   **G⁶** **Am⁹/G#**   **Am⁹**

And it's making me cry, and it's making me cry,

Fmaj¹³#¹¹   **G⁶** **Am⁹/G#**   **Am⁹**

And I'm slipping away, and I'm slipping away.

Coda

Am♭⁶   **G⁶/⁹**   **F⁶/⁹**

It's only superstition, only your imagination,

Am♭⁶   **G⁶/⁹**   **F⁶/⁹**

It's only superstition, only superstition.

See You Soon

Words & Music by
Guy Berryman, Jon Buckland, Will Champion & Chris Martin

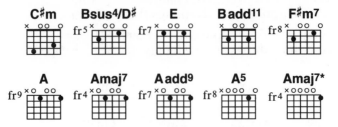

Tune guitar (from bottom string): F#, G, D, D, B, D,
Capo second fret

Intro

| C#m Bsus4/D# E | Badd11 | C#m Bsus4/D# E | Badd11 |

| C#m Bsus4/D# E | Badd11 | F#m7 E | Badd11 ‖

Verse 1

  C#m Bsus4/D# E   Badd11
  So you   lost your trust,

                C#m
And you never shared her,

     Bsus4/D# E   Badd11
And you   never shared her.

C#m Bsus4/D# E   Badd11
  But don't   break your back,

             C#m Bsus4/D# E   Badd11
If you ever see this,   don't   answer that.

Chorus 1

  A   Amaj7 Aadd9 Amaj7
  In a bullet - proof   vest,

          Badd11   A
With the windows all closed,

         Amaj7 Aadd9 Amaj7   A5
I'll be doing my   best, I'll see you soon

  A   Amaj7 Aadd9 Amaj7
  In a tele - scope   lens.

             Badd11   A5   Amaj7*
And when all you want is friends,   I'll see you soon.

Link 1

| C#m Bsus4/D# E | Badd11 | C#m Bsus4/D# E | Badd11 ‖

Verse 2

C#m Bsus4/D# E   Badd11
So they   came for you,

                        C#m
They came snapping at your heels,

    Bsus4/D#   E   Badd11
They come   snapping at your   heels.

C#m Bsus4/D# E   Badd11
But don't   break your back,

              C#m
If you ever say this,

    Bsus4/D# E   Badd11
But don't   answer that.

Chorus 2

    A   Amaj7 Aadd9 Amaj7
In a bullet - proof   vest,

        Badd11   A
With the windows all closed,

      Amaj7 Aadd9 Amaj7   A5
I'll be doing   my   best, I'll see you soon

A   Amaj7 Aadd9 Amaj7
In a tele - scope lens.

   Badd11   A5   Amaj7*
And when all you want is friends, I'll see you soon.

Link 2

| C#m Bsus4/D# E | Badd11 | C#m Bsus4/D# E | Badd11 |
                                       I'll see you soon.

| C#m Bsus4/D# E | Badd11 | C#m Bsus4/D# E | Badd11 ||

Coda

A5   E   Badd11
I know you lost your trust,

A5   E   Badd11
I know you lost your trust,

A5   E   Badd11
I know, don't lose your trust,

A5   E   Badd11
I know you lost your trust.

Sparks

Words & Music by
Guy Berryman, Jon Buckland, Will Champion & Chris Martin

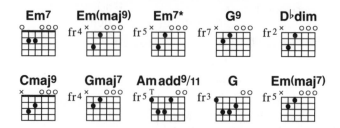

Capo sixth fret, tune top string down to D

Intro

| Em⁷* Em(maj⁹) | Em⁷/G G⁹ | D♭dim | Cmaj⁷ |

‖: Gmaj⁷ | Em⁷* | Gmaj⁷ | Em⁷* :‖

Verse 1

Gmaj⁷   Em⁷* Gmaj⁷
    Did I drive you away?
                                    Em⁷*
Well I know what you'll say,
                    Amadd⁹/11   Gmaj⁷ G Gmaj⁷
You'll say "Oh, sing one you know."
                              Em⁷* Gmaj⁷
But I promise you this,
                    Em⁷   Amadd⁹/11
I'll always look out for you,
                    Gmaj⁷
That's what I'll do.

Bridge 1

            Em⁷ Em(maj⁹) | Em⁷* G⁹ | D♭dim | Cmaj⁷ |
Say I, _____
            Em⁷ Em(maj⁹) | Em⁷* G⁹ | D♭dim | Cmaj⁷ ‖
And say I. _____

Link 1

‖: Gmaj⁷ | Em⁷* | Gmaj⁷ | Em⁷* :‖

Verse 2

     Gmaj7   **Em7*** **Gmaj7**
     My heart is yours,

         Em7*   **Am add9/11**
It s you that I hold on to,

        Gmaj7 **G** **Gmaj7**
That s what I do.

               Em7* **Em(maj7)** **Gmaj7**
And I know I was wrong,

        Em7
But I won t let you down.

Am add9/11   **Gmaj7** **G**
Oh yeah, I will, yeah I will, yes I will.

Bridge 2

   Em7 **Em(maj9)** | **Em7*** **G9** | **D♭dim** | **Cmaj7** |
I said I, ——————————

   Em7 **Em(maj9)** | **Em7*** **G9** | **D♭dim** | **Cmaj7**   ‖
I cry I. ——————————

Chorus

     Gmaj7   **Em7***
And I saw sparks,

     Gmaj7   **Em7***
Yeah I saw sparks,

   Gmaj7   **Em7***
I saw sparks,

     Gmaj7   **Em7***
Yeah I saw sparks,

    Gmaj7
See me now.

Coda

    Em7*   **Gmaj7**
La la la, la oh,

     Em7*   **Gmaj7**
La la la, la oh,

     Em7*   **Gmaj7**
La la la, la oh,

     Em7*   **Gmaj7**
La la la, la oh.

Spies

Words & Music by
Guy Berryman, Jon Buckland, Will Champion & Chris Martin

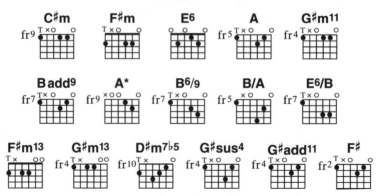

Tune guitar (from bottom string): E, A, C♯, G, B, C♯

Intro | C♯m | C♯m | C♯m | C♯m   ‖

Verse 1

F♯m   **E6**
I awake to find no peace of mind,
                    A   **G♯m11**
I said "How do you live as a fugitive?"
        F♯m   **E6**
Down here, where I cannot see so clear,
                    A
I said "What do I know?"
                        G♯m11
Show me the right way to go.

Chorus 1

            F♯m   **G♯m11**
And the spies came out of the water,
                A   **G♯m11**
But you're feeling so bad 'cause you know
            F♯m   **E6**
That the spies hide out in every corner,
                        A
But you can't touch them, no,
            B add9   **C♯m** | **A*** | **B6/9** **B add9** |
'Cause they're all spies
B6/9   **B add9** **C♯m** | **A*** | **B6/9** **B add9** | **B6/9** **B add9** ‖
They're all spies.

Verse 2

      F♯m   **E6**
I awake to see that no one is free,
           A   **G♯m11**
We're all fugitives, look at the way we live
      F♯m   **E6**
Down here, I cannot sleep from fear, no.
             A
I said "Which way do I turn?"
          G♯m11
Oh, I forget everything I learn.

Chorus 2   As Chorus 1

Bridge

  B/A   **A***   **E6/B**
   And if we don't hide here
              B add9 **F♯m13**
They're going to find us,
   G♯m13   **F♯m13**
If we don't hide now
              B add9   **B/A**
They're going to catch us where we sleep,
        A*   **E6/B**
And if we don't hide here
              B add9 | **D♯m7♭5** | **G♯sus4 G♯add11** ‖
They're going to find us. _____

Solo   ‖: **C♯m** | **A*** | **B6/9 B add9** | **B6/9 B add9** :‖

Chorus 3

  A   **G♯m11**
Spies came out of the water,
          B/A   **F♯**
And you're feeling so good 'cause you know
          F♯m   **E6**
That those spies hide out in every corner
                A
And they can't touch you, no,
        B add9
'Cause they're just spies,
 B6/9   **B add9 C♯m** | **A*** | **B6/9 B add9** |
They're just spies.

                                    Play 3 times
‖: **C♯m** | **A*** | **B6/9 B add9** | **B6/9**   **B add9** :‖
                                  They're just spies.

| **C♯m**   ‖

Such A Rush

Words & Music by
Guy Berryman, Jon Buckland, Will Champion & Chris Martin

Cm   F   Cm*   Cm6   Cm(maj7)   C5

Fm   Gm7♭6   G7   B♭   A♭maj7   G7sus4

Intro

‖: Cm | Cm F | Cm | Cm F :‖ *Play 3 times*

| Cm | Cm F | Cm | Cm |

Verse 1

Cm*   Cm6 Cm(maj7) C5   Cm6   Cm*
Such a rush   to do nothing at all,

     Cm6 Cm(maj7) C5   Cm6   Fm
Such a fuss   to do nothing at all,

     Gm7♭6   G7   Cm
Such a rush   to do nothing at all.

Verse 2

Cm*   Cm6 Cm(maj7) C5   Cm6   Cm*
Such a rush   to get nowhere at all,

     Cm6 Cm(maj7) C5   Cm6   Fm
Such a fuss   to do nothing at all,

     Gm7♭6   G7   Cm | Cm F ‖
Such a rush. _____

Chorus 1

     Fm   B♭
And it's just like you said,

   Fm   Gm7♮6 G7 Cm
It's just like you said. _____

Verse 3

Cm*   Cm6 Cm(maj7) C5   Cm6   Cm*
Such a rush   to do nothing at all,

     Cm6 Cm(maj7) C5   Cm6   Fm
Such a fuss   to get nowhere at all,

      Gm7♭6   G7 | Cm | Cm F ‖
Such a rush, such a rush

Chorus 2

    Fm   **B♭**
And it's just like you said,

   Fm   **Gm7♭6** **G7** **A♭maj7**
It's just like you said. _____

Bridge 1

     G7sus4 **G7** **A♭maj7**
Just slow down   please

     G7sus4 **G7** **A♭maj7**
Just slow down. _____

    G7sus4 **G7** **A♭maj7**
So slow down   please

   G7sus4 **G7** **C5** | **F** | **C5** | **F** ‖
Just slow   down. _____

Link | **C5** | **F** | **C5** | **F** ‖

Bridge 2

   C5   **F**
Such a rush, such a rush, such a rush, such a rush,

   C5   **F**
Such a rush, such a rush, such a rush, such a rush,

   C5   **F**
Such a rush, such a rush, such a rush, such a rush,

   C5   **F**
Such a rush, such a rush, such a rush.

Verse 4

   C5   **F**
Look at all the people going after money,

   C5   **F**
Far too many people looking for their money.

   C5   **F**
Everybody's out there, trying to get money.

   C5
Why can't you just tell me,

   F   **C5** **F**
Trying to get money, rush.

Verse 4

    C5 **F**
Such a rush,

     C5 **F**
They all rush,

    C5 **F**
Such a rush.

    C5   **F**
Such a rush, such a rush, such a rush, such a rush,

    C5   **F** **C5**
Such a rush, such a rush.

Trouble

Words & Music by
Guy Berryman, Jon Buckland, Will Champion & Chris Martin

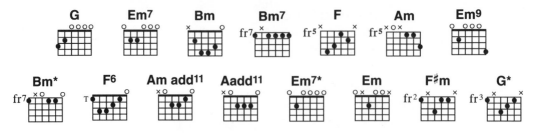

Tune top string down to D

Intro   ‖: G   Em7 | Bm | G   Em7 | Bm   :‖

Verse 1
       G   Em7 Bm7
       Oh no, I see,

          F   Am   G
       A spider web is tangled up with me,

           Em7   Bm7
       And I lost my head,

            F   Am   G
       And thought of all the stupid things I'd said.

Link 1 | G   Em7 | Bm | G   Em7 | Bm   ‖

Verse 2
       G   Em9   Bm*
       Oh no, what's this?

        F6   Am add11
       A spider web, and I'm caught in the middle,

       G   Em9   Bm*
       So I turn to run,

         F6   Am add11   G
       And thought of all the stupid things I'd done.

Chorus 1

Aadd¹¹ **Em⁷**

And ah, I never meant to cause you trouble,

Aadd¹¹ **Em⁷**

And ah, I never meant to do you wrong,

Aadd¹¹ **Em⁷**

And ah, well if I ever caused you trouble,

Aadd¹¹ **Em⁷**

Then oh, I never meant to do you harm.

Link 2 | **G   Em⁷** | **Bm** | **G   Em⁷** | **Bm**   ‖

Verse 3

G   Em⁹ Bm*

Oh no, I see,

F⁶ **Am add¹¹**

A spider web and it's me in the middle,

G   Em⁷   Bm*

So I twist and turn,

F⁶ **Am add¹¹** **G**

But here I am in my little bubble.

Chorus 2

Aadd¹¹ **Em⁷**

Singing out ah, I never meant to cause you trouble,

Aadd¹¹ **Em⁷**

And ah, I never meant to do you wrong,

Aadd¹¹ **Em⁷**

And ah, well if I ever caused you trouble,

Aadd¹¹ **Em⁷**

Then oh no I never meant to do you harm.

Link 3   ‖: **G   Em⁹** | **Bm*** | **G   Em⁹** | **Bm***   :‖

Coda

Em **F♯m   G* F♯m   Em**

And they spun a web for me,

F♯m   G* F♯m   Em

And they spun a web for me,

F♯m   G* F♯m   Em | **Em** |

And they spun a web for me.

‖: **G   Em⁷** | **Bm*** | **G   Em⁷** | **Bm***   :‖

We Never Change

Words & Music by
Guy Berryman, Jon Buckland, Will Champion & Chris Martin

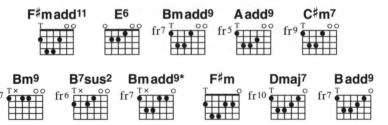

Tune guitar (from bottom string): **E, A, D, G, B, C#**

Intro   ‖: F#madd11 | F#madd11 | E6 | E6 :‖

Verse 1

        F#madd11   E6
I wanna live life and never be cruel,

           F#madd11   E6
And I wanna live life and be good to you,

      Bmadd9 F#madd11   E6
And I wanna   fly and never come down,

      Bmadd9 F#madd11   E6   Aadd9
And live my   life and have friends around.

Chorus 1

                     C#m7   Aadd9
But we never change, do we? No, no,

              C#m7
We never learn, do we?

      Bmadd9 F#madd11   E6
So I wanna   live in a wooden house.

Verse 2

        F#madd11   E6
I wanna live life and always be true,

        F#madd11   E6
I wanna live life and be good to you,

Bmadd9 F#madd11   E6
I wanna   fly and never come down,

      Bmadd9 F#madd11   E6   Aadd9
And live my   life and have friends around.

Chorus 2	**C♯m⁷** **Aadd⁹**

Chorus 2

                           C♯m⁷   **Aadd⁹**

But we never change, do we? No, no,

                          C♯m⁷

We never learn, do we?

          Bmadd⁹   **F♯madd¹¹**   **E⁶**

So I wanna live in a wooden house,

                Bmadd⁹   **F♯madd¹¹**   **E⁶**

Where making more friends would be easy.

Bridge

          Bm⁹   **B⁷sus²** **Bm⁹**   **B⁷sus²** **E⁶**   **Bm⁹**

               Oh, I don't have a soul to   save,

       B⁷sus²   **Bm⁹**   **B⁷sus²**   **E⁶** **Bmadd⁹**

        Yes, and I sin every single day.

Chorus 3

          F♯madd¹¹   **E⁶**   **Bmadd⁹**

We never change, do we?

          F♯madd¹¹   **E⁶**

We never learn, do we?

Outro

          Bmadd⁹ **F♯m**   **E⁶**   **Bmadd⁹***

So I wanna live in a wooden house,

                             F♯m   **Dmaj⁷**   **Badd⁹**

Where making more friends would be ea - sy.

       Bmadd⁹   **F♯m**   **E⁶**   **Bmadd⁹**

I wanna live where the sun comes out.

Yellow

Words & Music by
Guy Berryman, Jon Buckland, Will Champion & Chris Martin

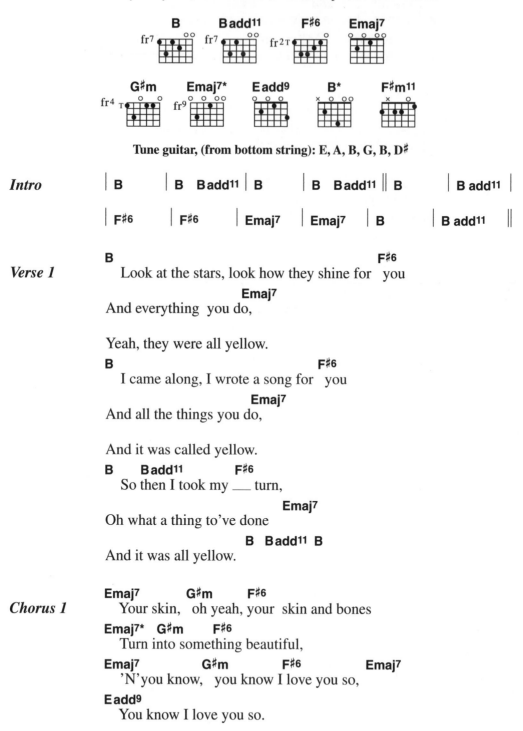

Tune guitar, (from bottom string): E, A, B, G, B, D#

Intro
| B | B Badd11 | B | B Badd11 ‖ B | B add11 |
| F#6 | F#6 | Emaj7 | Emaj7 | B | B add11 ‖

Verse 1

    B   F#6
Look at the stars, look how they shine for you
                     Emaj7
And everything you do,

Yeah, they were all yellow.
 B   F#6
I came along, I wrote a song for you
                   Emaj7
And all the things you do,

And it was called yellow.
 B   Badd11   F#6
So then I took my ＿ turn,
                     Emaj7
Oh what a thing to've done
                   B Badd11 B
And it was all yellow.

Chorus 1

Emaj7   G#m   F#6
Your skin,   oh yeah, your skin and bones
Emaj7* G#m   F#6
Turn into something beautiful,
Emaj7   G#m   F#6   Emaj7
'N'you know, you know I love you so,
E add9
You know I love you so.

Link 1 | B | B | F♯6 | F♯6 |

            | Emaj7 | Emaj7 | B | B ||

Verse 2
B   F♯6
    I swam across, I jumped across for   you,
                                  Emaj7
Oh, what a thing to do

'Cause you were all yellow.
B   Badd11   F♯6
    I drew a line, I drew a line for   you,
                            Emaj7
Oh, what a thing to do
                            B   Badd11   B
And it was all yellow.

Chorus 2
Emaj7   G♯m   F♯6
    Your skin,   oh yeah, your skin and bones
Emaj7*   G♯m   F♯6
    Turn into something beautiful,
Emaj7   G♯m   F♯6   Emaj7
    'N'you know?   For you I bleed myself dry,
Eadd9
    For you I bleed myself (dry.)

Link 2 | B | B | F♯6 | F♯6 |
            dry.

            | Emaj7 | Emaj7 | B | B ||

Coda
        B   F♯6
It's true, look how they shine for you,
                            Emaj7
Look how they shine for you, look how they shine for,
B   F♯6
    Look how they shine for you,
                            Emaj7
Look how they shine for you, look how they shine.
B*
    Look at the stars,
                            F♯madd11
Look how they shine for   you
                            Emaj7
And all the things that you __ do.

Shiver

Words & Music by
Guy Berryman, Jon Buckland, Will Champion & Chris Martin

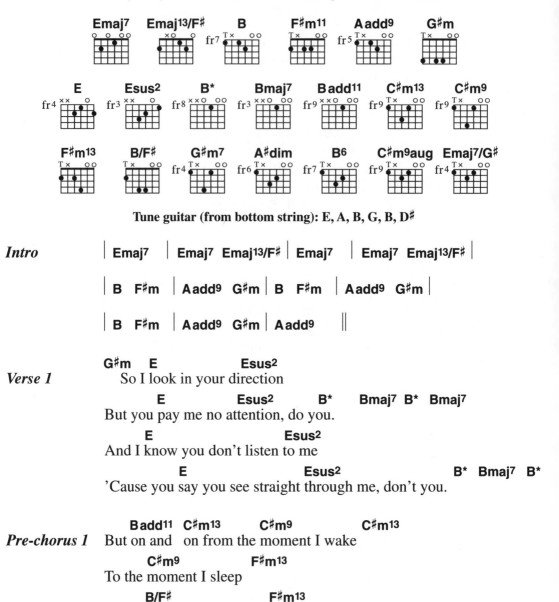

Tune guitar (from bottom string): E, A, B, G, B, D#

Intro | Emaj7 | Emaj7   Emaj13/F# | Emaj7 | Emaj7   Emaj13/F# |

           | B   F#m | Aadd9   G#m | B   F#m | Aadd9   G#m |

           | B   F#m | Aadd9   G#m | Aadd9 |

Verse 1
G#m   E   Esus2
So I look in your direction
        E   Esus2   B*   Bmaj7 B* Bmaj7
But you pay me no attention, do you.
        E   Esus2
And I know you don't listen to me
            E   Esus2   B* Bmaj7 B*
'Cause you say you see straight through me, don't you.

Pre-chorus 1
        Badd11 C#m13   C#m9   C#m13
But on and   on from the moment I wake
        C#m9   F#m13
To the moment I sleep
        B/F#   F#m13
I'll be there by your side,
            B/F#   C#m13
Just you try and stop me.
                                            B   G#m7
I'll be waiting in line just to see if you care, oh whoa.

cont.

        A♯dim   **B6**
Did you want me to change?

        A♯dim   **G♯m7**
Well I'd change for good.

      A♯dim   **B6**
And I want you to know

           C♯m9aug   **B6**
That you'll always get your way.

   A♯dim   **G♯m7**   **Emaj7/G♯**
I wanted to say;

Chorus 1

                B **F♯m11** **Aadd9** **G♯m**
Don't you shiver,

        B6 **F♯m11** **Aadd9** **G♯m**
Shiver,

         B **Aadd9**   **G♯m7**
Shiver,   ooh. _____

      Aadd9   **G♯m**
I'll always be waiting for you.

Verse 2

        E   **Esus2**
So you know how much I need you

        E   **Esus2**   **B***   **Bmaj7** **B*** **Bmaj7**
But you never even see me, do you?

        E   **Esus2** **E**   **Esus2** **B*** **Bmaj7** **B***
And is this my final   chance of getting you?

Pre-chorus 2

      Badd11 **C♯m13**   **C♯m9**   **C♯m13**
But on and   on from the moment I wake

      C♯m9   **F♯m13**
To the moment I sleep

      B/F♯   **F♯m13**
I'll be there by your side,

        B/F♯   **C♯m13**
Just you try and stop me.

                       B   **G♯m7**
I'll be waiting in line just to see if you care, oh whoa.

      A♯dim   **B6**
Did you want me to change?

      A♯dim   **G♯m7**
Well I'd change for good.

      A♯dim   **B6**
And I want you to know

         C♯m9aug   **B6**
That you'll always get your way.

   A♯dim   **G♯m7**   **Emaj7/G♯**
I wanted to say;

Chorus 2

             B F♯m11 Aadd9 G♯m
Don't you shiver,

       B6 F♯m11 Aadd9 G♯m
Shiver,

       B Aadd9   G♯m7
Shiver,   ooh. _____

   Aadd9   **G♯m**
I'll always be waiting for you.

| **Emaj7** | **Emaj7** | **Emaj7** | ‖

Bridge

          B   **Aadd9**   **Emaj7**
Yeah, I'll always be waiting for you,

          B   **Aadd9**   **Emaj7**
Yeah, I'll always be waiting for you,

          B   **Aadd9**   **Emaj7**
Yeah, I'll always be waiting for you,

For you, I will always be waiting.

        B   **F♯m11**   **Aadd9**   **G♯m**
And it's you I see but you don't see me,

        B   **F♯m11** **Aadd9**   **G♯m**
And it's you I hear so loud and clear.

        B   **F♯m11** **Aadd9** **G♯m**
I sing it loud __ and clear

       Aadd9   **G♯m**
And I'll always be waiting for you.

Verse 3

       Emaj7   **Esus2**
So I look in your direction

        Emaj7   **Esus2**
But you pay me no attention.

         Emaj7   **Esus2**
And you know how much I need you

        Emaj7   **Esus2**
But you never even see me.